*Newman History and Philosophy
of Science Series*

PIONEERS OF PREHISTORY
IN ENGLAND

*Newman History and Philosophy
of Science Series*

GENERAL EDITOR: P. E. HODGSON

10

PIONEERS OF PREHISTORY
IN ENGLAND

by
L. K. CLARK, O.P., F.G.S.

SHEED AND WARD
LONDON AND NEW YORK

FIRST PUBLISHED 1961
UNDER THE AUSPICES
OF THE NEWMAN ASSOCIATION OF GREAT BRITAIN
(PHILOSOPHY OF SCIENCE GROUP)
SHEED AND WARD LTD.
33 MAIDEN LANE
LONDON, W.C.2
AND
SHEED AND WARD INC.
64 UNIVERSITY PLACE
NEW YORK 3

©

L. K. CLARK, O.P., 1961

THIS BOOK IS SET IN 12 ON 13-PT. BASKERVILLE TYPE
PRINTED AND MADE IN GREAT BRITAIN BY
FLETCHER AND SON LTD., AND
THE LEIGHTON-STRAKER BOOKBINDING CO. LTD., LONDON

IN MEMORY OF
WILLIAM PENGELLY, F.G.S., F.R.S.
TO WHOSE LITERATURE OF KENT'S CAVERN
IN THE
TRANSACTIONS OF THE DEVONSHIRE ASSOCIATION
THE AUTHOR
IS MUCH INDEBTED

ABBREVIATIONS

AE   *Archaeologia*

JGSL   *Journal of the Geological Society of London*

PGSL   *Proceedings of the Geological Society of London*

PTRS   *Philosophical Transactions of the Royal Society*

TDA   *Report and Transactions of the Devonshire Association for the Advancement of Science, Literature and Art*, Plymouth, 1863—

TGSL   *Transactions of the Geological Society of London*

CONTENTS

FOREWORD

Although the antiquity of man was discovered in the first quarter of the nineteenth century, it did not receive public
acceptance by the scientific world till
1859. Modern books on the subject can
give in their introductions only a brief
notice of the early pioneer work in England
that led up to this event.

A fuller account from original sources
now seems fitting, particularly as 1959 was
the centenary year of Sir Joseph Prestwich's classical memoir which brought
about the acceptance of what we now call
prehistory.

EARLY STUDIES IN PREHISTORY IN ENGLAND: REV. JOHN MACENERY'S WORK

If the Reverend John MacEnery (1796-1841), an obscure Catholic priest of Torquay, had not died prematurely, he might have been honoured at the present day with the title of Father of English Prehistory. During the 1820's, he made discoveries which undoubtedly proved the existence in England of a prehistoric race of man more ancient than that hitherto known to archaeologists — Palaeolithic Man. But the conservatism of the scientific world of his day little encouraged him to press home his discoveries; while lack of funds and ill-health prevented him from bringing them before the public in book form.

As a foreword to the story of MacEnery's "Systematic observations of Kent's Hole and other Caverns" in South Devon, of which his monument in the parish churchyard of Tor proclaims him to have been the pioneer, one must recall the state, at that period, of this type of scientific investigation.

In the first quarter of the nineteenth century geology was but emerging from an elementary stage. It was still dominated by the old idea of a world of which the surface had been fashioned by a series of devastating cataclysms, each followed by a fresh creation of new forms of animals and plants: the Deluge was the latest. But, for all that, geology was beginning to unveil, in the history of the globe, long periods which no one had ever before suspected even to exist. Of cave research there had been a fair amount of investigation on the Continent: Cuvier's marvellous identification of the extinct mammalia from fossil fragments had given it further impetus. In England, papers had been read to the Royal Society in 1817[1] and 1821,[2] describing fossil bones discovered by workmen while quarrying limestone at Oreston Cave for the Plymouth breakwater. But it

[1] Sir Everard Home, "An Account of some fossil remains of the Rhinoceros, discovered by Mr Whitby, in a cavern inclosed in the limestone rock, from which he is forming the Breakwater at Plymouth", *PTRS* (1817), pp. 176-82.

[2] Joseph Whidbey, "A Further Account of fossil bones in caverns inclosed in the limestone rocks at Plymouth", *PTRS* (1821), pp. 133-4.

was Dr Buckland, in 1822, who was the
first in this country "to make these dry
bones live", when in his lecture[1] to the
same society, he described the hyena den
of Kirkdale, in the Vale of Pickering.
From the fossil bones found there he con-
clusively demonstrated, in his inimitable,
vivid style, that, at some very remote
period, hyenas had dragged into the
Yorkshire cave the remains of elephant,
rhinoceros, hippopotamus, bear, tiger and
other species. Many of his hearers were
surprised to learn that wild beasts of an
apparently warmer climate had once
roamed the hills and dales of the Yorkshire
moors. When MacEnery commenced his
researches, Buckland was an acknowledged
authority, at home and abroad. His book
Reliquiae Diluvianae (1823) was a splendid
quarto with plates illustrating fossils, and
pictorial sections of twenty-one caves
which he had explored or visited in England and Germany. Boyd Dawkins (1874)

[1] Rev. William Buckland, "Account of an assemblage of
Fossil Teeth and Bones of Elephant, Rhinoceros, Hippopotamus, Bear, Tiger, and Hyaena, and sixteen other animals;
discovered in a cave of Kirkdale, Yorkshire, in the year 1821:
with a comparative view of five similar caverns in various
parts of England, and others on the Continent" (with plates),
PTRS (1822), pp. 171-236.

said that "it laid the foundations of the new science of cave-hunting in this country".[1]

A quotation from MacEnery's writings will serve to record his early impressions of cave exploration. His first visit to Kent's Cavern was in the company of the eccentric Thomas Northmore, who in the previous year had discovered there fossil remains of animals.[2]

To the following incident I am indebted for first directing my steps towards the Cavern:—Having one morning in the summer of 1825 chanced to hear a friend (the late Captain Welby) express his intention to join an exploring party there, I was induced to accompany him. We found his relation Mr Northmore ... at its entrance, surrounded by about a dozen persons, among whom were remarked the Commander of the coastguard and his men. All busy in equipping themselves for their expedition underground.

The passage being too narrow to

[1] W. Boyd Dawkins, *Cave Hunting*, London, 1874, p. 14.
[2] There is an account of this in a letter published in *TDA*, vol. 2, pp. 479-91.

admit more than one person at a time
(and that only in a stooping posture)
the company entered in files, each bearing a light in one hand and a pickaxe in
the other, headed by a guide, carrying
a lantern before the chief of the band. I
made the last of the train, for I could
not divest myself of certain undefinable
sensations, it being my first visit to a
scene of this nature.[1]

From this account it appears that the
explorers dug the stalagmite flooring with
their pickaxes in search of fossils, but
found none. MacEnery at once realized
that superficial excavations were useless,
and, seeking a more suitable spot by himself, dug in the ground and was successful:

They were the first fossil teeth I had
ever seen, and as I laid my hand on
them, relics of extinct [animal] races
and witnesses of an order of things which
passed away with them, I shrank back
involuntarily.—Though not insensible
to the excitement attending new discoveries, I am not ashamed to own that in

[1] J. MacEnery, "Cavern Researches", *TDA*, vol. 3 (1869),
p. 208.

the presence of these remains I felt more of awe than joy—but whatever may have been [the] impressions or the speculations that naturally rushed into my mind, this is not the place to divulge them.—My present business is with facts.

I pursued my search in silence and kept my good fortune a secret, fearing that amidst the press and avidity of the party to possess some fossil memorial of the day, my discoveries would be damaged or perhaps share the fate of those abstracted [on a previous visit] from Mr Northmore's basket.[1]

These specimens he sent to Buckland, at Oxford, whose response was a letter "which urged me to follow up my good luck".[2] A plate to illustrate the fossils and some further discoveries was engraved and published as "Teeth and bones found in Kent's Hole, near Torquay, Devon by the Revd. I. McEnery, in October 1825."

Encouraged by the success of his first ventures, MacEnery undertook a systematic excavation of the extensive series

[1] MacEnery, p. 210.   [2] MacEnery, p. 210.

of limestone caves, formerly known as Kent's Hole and now as Kent's Cavern, which range over an area of many hundred square feet. To quote his own words:

Its contents moreover lay generally at considerable depths and were rendered nearly inaccessible by the thickness of the stalagmitic floor which everywhere overspread them—no satisfactory results could therefore be augured from a superficial search here and there—a thorough examination both of the main branches and of the most intricate involutions and secret recesses where many of the precious relics lie concealed—yet remained a desideratum in science. Stimulated by former success, I did not hesitate a moment to undertake it—but the work demanded a large acquaintance with similar phenomena and a constitution inured to fatigue and proof against the chills incident to sustained exertions in unwholesome vaults.—In defect of others better qualified to accomplish the investigation, I commenced digging at the close of 1825, and with little interruption have continued it down to the present time[1] with unabated spirit.[2]

Much can be done by an enthusiast, and this is exceptionally true of MacEnery: his discoveries were countless. Within one year he had presented collections of his finds to museums in London, Paris, Bristol and York. In the last of these institutions there is still MacEnery's accompanying memoir, with comments on the specimens by Cuvier and Buckland.[3] On April 6th of the following year, 1827, the Geological Society of London conferred on him the distinction of election to its fellowship—he was then thirty years old—and some time later the same honour was bestowed on him by the Geological Society of France.

For five years he toiled incessantly, sometimes alone, but often assisted by workmen, friends, or well-known geologists, exploring not only Kent's Cavern, but also many of the ossiferous limestone caves of South Devon—Anstey's Cove, Chudleigh Rock, Buckfastleigh, Oreston

[1] Probably 1828.   [2] MacEnery, pp. 443-4.
[3] Published in *TDA*, vol. 4 (1870-1), pp. 471-7.

Cave and Berry Head. Throughout all these researches he kept in touch with Buckland and the brilliant French palae-ontologist Cuvier, to whom on different occasions he presented three collections of fossils of extinct mammalia.

That he was no mere wholesale collector of the enormous quantity of organic remains which he brought to light is evident from the long essays which were intended to accompany the drawings and plates of his unpublished work. From these it is clear that he had studied his finds minutely and had in time acquired an expert knowledge of cavern palaeontology. He was the first to discover in the British Isles the terrible sabre-toothed tiger, *Machairodus latidens*. In effect, he may be regarded as one of the founders in this country of its Pleistocene palaeontology.

Although his discoveries of the extinct animal inhabitants of the cavern were remarkable, yet those of its prehistoric human inhabitants were more so. He maintained that not only had he found in the cavern rude flint implements which were unmistakably fashioned by the hand of man, but also that these artefacts lay

beneath a thick unbroken sheet of stalagmite. Therefore they had been deposited
before the formation of the stalagmite and
seemed to be in association with the fossils
of the extinct fauna. To us in the twentieth
century there is nothing startling in this
statement. But to our forefathers, more
than a century ago, it was astounding. It
was putting back the arrival of the human
species in Britain to an epoch of time of
which there were no records in ancient
history, biblical or otherwise. It even
seemed to suggest what was unbelievable
—that primeval man had been the contemporary of the extinct animals. In order
to avoid the consequences of this discovery,
Buckland was "inclined to attribute the
flints to a more modern date by supposing
that the Ancient Britons had scooped out
ovens in the stalagmite and that through
them the [flint] knives got admission into
the diluvium [the stratum beneath the
stalagmite]."[1]

This hypothesis MacEnery proved to be
untenable by a long series of careful
excavations beneath stalagmite which,
without doubt, had never been broken

[1] MacEnery, p. 334.

into. His different tests for detecting virgin
stalagmite need not be detailed here, but a
paragraph connected with this question
(from the account of a later excavation) is
of interest:

> Having cleared away on all sides the
> loose mould and all suspicious appear-
> ances, I dug under the regular crust
> [unbroken stalagmite]—and flints pre-
> sented themselves in my hand—this
> electrified me—I called the attention of
> my fellow laborer [Master Aliffe] and
> in his presence extracted from the red
> marl arrow and lance heads.[1]

His next attempt was where the stalagmite
was two feet thick:

> About three inches below the crust, the
> tooth of an ox met my eye—I called the
> people to witness the fact—which I
> extracted before Master Aliffe—and not
> knowing the chance of finding flints I
> then proceeded to dig under it and at
> about a foot I dug out a flint arrow
> head. This confirmation I confess
> startled me—I dug again, and behold a

[1] MacEnery, p. 329.

second, of the same size and color (black). I struck my hammer into the earth a third time, and a third arrow head (but white) answered to the blow —This was evidence beyond all question—I then desisted—not wishing to exhaust the bed—but in case of cavil, leaving others an opportunity of verifying my statements.[1]

He ends the long discussion with the words:

It is painful to dissent from so high an authority [Buckland], and more particularly so from my concurrence generally in his views of the phenomena of these caves, which three years' personal observation had in almost every instance enabled me to verify.[2]

Before continuing the further development of this problem, it may be useful to add a quotation to indicate MacEnery's scrupulous care in noting the exact geological position of all his finds:

It is generally agreed that for solving

[1] MacEnery, pp. 329-30.   [2] MacEnery, p. 338.

the problem of their original introduction and their subsequent interment in these caves, and ascertaining the epoch of these changes, it is essential to know precisely the position and character of the remains at the time of their exhumation—(circumstances apparently unimportant—but which alone at this distance of time can lead to a final judgment on these points).[1]

The further development of the question follows naturally from the quotation about flint implements already given. The flints generally lay in the upper layers of the cave earth that contained the extinct fauna, yet they sometimes occurred with the fossils. Why, therefore, did not MacEnery infer what seems to us the evident conclusion, which later was suggested by Godwin-Austen, that Man was the contemporary of the mammoth and cave hyena? Was it because MacEnery was so intent on proving the priority of the flints to the stalagmite covering that he overlooked the full significance of their position beneath it?

[1] MacEnery, p. 442.

This was not in fact the case. He says:

> While I incline to the opinion of the post-diluvian origin of these flints [man posterior to the extinct mammalia], I feel obliged in candor to state the ground which would seem to countenance the opposite hypothesis,—as exhibited in the circumstances of the knives.[1]

He then gives three "circumstances" which favour the view that the flints belong to the stratum of the extinct fauna. To this discussion alone he devotes fifteen out of the thirty-five manuscript pages on flint implements. But the problem of the priority of the flints to the stalagmite was child's play, compared with the more complicated question whether their position demonstrated that the human species in England was co-existent with the now extinct mammalia. To point out that the flint occurred among the fossils would not in his day have been considered sufficient evidence—even if it could have been satisfactorily shown that the association of flint implements and bones of extinct animals was not due to

[1] MacEnery, p. 331.

later disturbances, and a commingling
into one promiscuous heap of the deposits
of wholly different eras.

This indeed was the crux of the difficulty so hotly debated in later years. As
late as 1853 Lyell was writing in the ninth
edition of his *Principles of Geology*, for the
synopsis at the heading of Chapter 46:
"Intermixture, in caves of South of France
and elsewhere, of human remains and
bones of extinct quadrupeds, no proof of
former co-existence of man with those lost
species." As these caves in the past had
often been the channels of engulfed rivers,
he discusses the various ways in which it
might be possible for relics of one period to
become associated with those of an older
date, and be again sealed up under stalagmite. No one could accuse the much-
travelled Lyell of being an armchair geologist, incapable of judging the evidence
with an open and just mind. We know
now that his verdict was correct in most of
the instances where it was a case of
evidence solely based on human fossils.

Today we recognize the valuable testimony of Palaeolithic flints, but more than
a century ago Buckland and Cuvier had

little knowledge of their probable significance. Their science of prehistoric archaeology had grown up from their painstaking
study of fossil remains; and therefore for
them the only real evidence would have
been human fossil bones unequivocally
occurring with those of the extinct mammalia. Lyell, in 1830, argued that if man
had existed in the time of the extinct
animals then his remains would be found
fairly frequently. "No inhabitant of the
land exposes himself to so many dangers
on the water as man, whether in a savage
or a civilized state, and there is no animal,
therefore, whose skeleton is so liable to
become imbedded in lacustrine or sub-
marine deposits."[1]

MacEnery's great difficulty, therefore,
was the lack of corroborative evidence
from human remains. He says:

I too have found human bones near the
mouth [inside the cave]—accompanied
with pottery, shells and an ornament
made of bone. They were entombed in a
pit excavated in the surface of stalagmite, indicating comparatively modern

[1] C. Lyell, *Principles of Geology*, 1st ed., London, 1830, p. 154.

sepulture ... but in the decidedly diluvium deposit, no human tooth or bone
has revealed itself.—Over and over
again have I [reviewed] at my leisure
every individual tooth and bone of my
immense collection. ... From all which
it may be [collected] that man did not
... co-exist in this country with the
animal population.[1]

This conspicuous absence of human fossils
among such an enormous quantity of
fossils—running into thousands—was too
cogent an argument for MacEnery. Nevertheless, he concludes by saying:

From this period more especially,—
March, 1827—I attached still greater
importance to their presence [the
worked flints], carefully, cautiously and
deliberately scrutinized and noted their
localities, and looked for fixed and
settled grounds for building my opinion
upon—but this evidence is not perhaps yet complete—future enquirers
may hereafter light on some more
decided document to define their epoch.[2]

[1] MacEnery, p. 333.   [2] MacEnery, p. 339 (Fasc. D).

In his essays on flint implements it is not a little surprising to find that he anticipated the distinction of type which was later termed Palaeolithic and Neolithic. In the upper deposits of the floor of the cave, beneath a layer which he classed as coeval with the Roman epoch, he found rude pottery, polished celts and articles made of bone. But in the lower deposits, beneath a thick layer of stalagmite, were the flints of which he says:

> None of the cavern blades appeared to have been rubbed or polished, but exhibit the rough serrated edge of the original fracture—this difference alone may not be sufficient to authorize us in assigning to the [cavern] reliquiae ... a higher antiquity—but the absence of other Druidical remains at the depth where the flints abound is a negative confirmation. ...[1]

And again:

> The circumstance of their being of ruder workmanship than the sepulchral relics [barrows] ... inclines us to refer them

[1] MacEnery, p. 477.

to an earlier date—to the progenitors of
those Celts who founded the barrows ...[1]

Again he writes:

It is strange that flint knives have not
been found intermixed with [artefacts]
... on the surface—nor pottery found
with the knives under the crust. ...[2]
It is singular that they never have been
traced upwards in the direction of the
surface.[3] ... A nomadic people, strangers
to even the rude pottery of a later
period.[4] ... In their time metal would
seem to have been yet unknown, or if
known not used. They were the mere
savage nomads in the very infancy of a
renewed race, to whom life was yet little
removed from the condition of the
beasts they pursued.[5]

He had even advanced so far in his study
of Palaeolithic implements as to classify
them in a three-fold division somewhat
analogous to the three headings under
which Evans grouped the flint implements
of Abbeville and Amiens in 1859:

[1] MacEnery, p. 339.   [2] MacEnery, p. 478.
[3] MacEnery, p. 327.   [4] MacEnery, p. 433.
              [5] MacEnery, p. 298.

... [flakes] pointed at one end ... used as arrow-heads, spear and lance heads.[1]
... oblong double-edged splinters, plain on one surface but raised on the obverse ... truncated at their extremities.[2]
... oval-shaped disks chipped round to an edge from two to $3\frac{1}{2}$ inches across, and some of them diminished to a point, like wedges. This part in these specimens was observed to be blunted, apparently from knocking like a hammer against hard bodies—while the sides, which in such an operation would not be used, still remained sharp.— They are obtuse and massive on one side, but sliced to an edge at the opposite.[3]

Evans says in his *Ancient Stone Implements* (1872):

It is not a little remarkable that among the nine specimens selected for engraving by Mr MacEnery, and given in his

[1] J. Evans, "Occurrence of Flint Implements in undisturbed beds of gravel, sand and clay", *AE*, vol. 38, pp. 289-92.
[2] MacEnery, p. 321. (These he considers may have been employed as knives or chisels.)
[3] MacEnery, p. 322.

Plate T as knives, arrow-heads and hatchets of flint and chert found in Kent's Hole, Torquay, three are of a distinctly Palaeolithic type, and two presumably so, the others being mere flakes, but of a character quite in accordance with their belonging to the same period as the better-defined types.[1]

To appreciate the value of MacEnery's researches, it must be remembered that while much excellent work had been carried out during his time in cavern explorations, very little had been achieved in the study of the concurrence of flint implements and the fossils of extinct animals. It is true, for example, that Dr Johnson, in his *Journey to the Western Islands* (1773), had remarked that the ancient stone arrow-heads found in Raasay "must have been made by a nation to whom the use of metals was unknown". This opinion was no novelty to the archaeologists of his time. They recognized that these flint arrows and axes were not "thunderbolts", but the tools or weapons

[1] J. Evans, *The Ancient Stone Implements, Weapons and Ornaments of Great Britain*, London, 1872, p. 443.

of a very primitive people who lived before the age of metals. But the stone implements with which they were acquainted were mostly of the Neolithic type, which clearly showed evidence of design in their polished uniform shape.

One noticeable exception is the historic Palaeolithic flint found about 1690 by John Conyers, antiquarian and apothecary, near Gray's Inn Lane, in a gravel-pit. A contemporary account says it was fastened into a shaft of good length; and not far from the place "the body of an Elephant" was dug out. But the real antiquity of this find was unsuspected for over a century and a half.

A still more remarkable exception was the discovery, in 1797, by John Frere, F.R.S., of a great number of these flints in the diggings of a brickfield near the village of Hoxne in Suffolk. The workmen had previously unearthed in a layer of sand above them "some extraordinary bones, particularly a jaw-bone of enormous size, of some unknown animal …"[1] With unusual insight, Frere wrote a letter, as short as it is interesting, to the Secretary

[1] *AE*, vol. 13 (1800), p. 204.

of the Society of Antiquaries of London, stating that the flints, "if not particularly objects of curiosity in themselves, must, I think, be considered in that light from the situation in which they were found".[1] Their geological position, he argued, "may tempt us to refer them to a very remote period indeed; even beyond that of the present world ... (and earlier).[2] They are, I think, evidently weapons of war, fabricated and used by a people who had not the use of metals. They lay in great numbers at the depth of about twelve feet, in stratified soil. ..."[3] This letter, with illustrative plates of definitely Palaeolithic type, appeared in *Archaeologia* for 1800 (vol. 13, pp. 204-5). Although specimens of the flints were presented to the British Museum and to that of the Society of Antiquaries, the discovery never seems to have aroused further interest, and the incident was forgotten until 1859.

Mention must be made of Dr Schmerling of Liége, who, in 1829, began to explore the bone caves on the banks of the Meuse and its tributaries. From the

---

[1] *AE*, vol. 13 (1800), p. 204.   [2] *AE*, vol. 13 (1800), p. 205.
[3] *AE*, vol. 13 (1800), p. 204.

discovery of human bones and flint flakes in the caves of Engis and Engihoul, he arrived at the conclusion that man was living at the remote time of the mammoth, rhinoceros, cave bear and hyena. In his *Recherches sur les ossemens fossiles* (1833-4) he has a short chapter in the second volume entitled, "Des débris travaillés par la main de l'Homme". He declares that in all caverns where there is an abundance of fossil bones he has also found a quantity, more or less, of worked flints. From their shape and design he has no doubt they are genuine artefacts. Therefore, he concludes, even if human bones had never been discovered to prove that man was coeval with the extinct animals, nevertheless these flints would have furnished sufficient proof of such a supposition.[1] "For the rest, time alone will decide how far we are right in expressing ourselves in such a categorical manner."

Considering, therefore, the advance that MacEnery had already made in his study of Palaeolithic flint implements during those early decades of the nineteenth

[1] P. C. Schmerling, *Recherches sur les ossemens fossiles découverts dans les cavernes de la province de Liége*, Liege, 1833-4, vol. 2, p. 179.

century, and in view of the fact that the
question of the antiquity of man was eventually settled, not by his fossil remains but
by the works of his hands, MacEnery
deserves a place among the pioneers of
prehistory. He was the first to find flint
implements in a cave associated with the
bones of extinct animals, and to realize
the significance of the discovery.

MacEnery's Attempts to Publish his Discoveries

It has been asserted several times that
MacEnery "did not dare even to publish
his records". This statement calls for an
account of his attempts to put into print
his finds and their implications. There is
no doubt that the idea of a primeval race
of men coeval with animals unknown to
ancient history did not fit in with the
archaeology of his age. There was a host of
learned volumes on ancient camps and
barrows, and so-called Druidic remains, of
what were considered the first primitive

people who had inhabited western Europe before the period of classical times. It seemed incredible to postulate a still earlier period of man before the dawn of history or oral tradition. It meant presuming the existence of a very ancient race of men on the mere evidence of rudely chipped flints which, some even maintained, could have been shaped by "the mysterious forces of nature". A later writer expressed the natural reactions which would arise in the minds of many when he said:

> We have more positive evidence that his [man's] first appearance was characterized by many proofs of high intellectual condition which our sacred beliefs attach to his origin, and that he was not primarily the ignoble creature that arrow-heads and flint-knives, and ossiferous caverns would so lamentably indicate.[1]

Milton's interpretation, in his unforgettable epic, of the Days of Creation, had a

[1] Dr Anderson, in the *Report of the 29th Meeting of the British Association*, Aberdeen, 1859, p. 96.

more powerful influence than was realized.

Nevertheless MacEnery did attempt to bring before the public the results of his cavern researches. Of this we have ample evidence.

Writing to Sir Walter Trevelyan, on 19 June 1826, MacEnery says:

Some plain account I intend to publish when the professor [Buckland] returns. Mrs Buckland purposes doing us the honour of a visit, when I hope to have collected abundant materials for her pencil [she was to draw the illustrations].[1]

On 6 December of the same year, Dr Beeke (later Bishop of Bath and Wells), in a letter to Sir Walter Trevelyan, says:

Mr MacEnery has arranged his Kent's Hole collection very neatly. ... He has prepared the materials for an account of the Cave, so far as his own observations extend, but waits for Dr Buckland's advice and assistance, and

[1] *TDA*, vol. 10 (1878), p. 144.

no drawings have yet been made of the
more important bones.[1]

A year later, on 16 November 1827, Sir
Henry de la Beche (then Mr), in a paper
read to the Geological Society of London
on "Tor and Babbacombe Bays",[2] mentions "Kent's Cavern, lately celebrated on
account of the remains of elephants,
rhinoceroses, hyenas, bears, deer, wolves,
etc., found in it".[3] In a footnote to the
paper, published in 1829, he adds:

The Reverend John McEnery, who
has formed a very valuable collection of
these remains, intends, I believe, to
publish an account of them; and Professor Buckland will probably do the
same in the continuation of his *Reliquiae
Diluvianae.*[4]

MacEnery had occasionally accompanied
De la Beche on his geological surveys.

By the year 1828 MacEnery had prepared an account of his researches, much

[1] *TDA*, vol. 10 (1878), p. 145.
[2] Henry Thomas de la Beche, "On the geology of the Tor
and Babbacombe Bays, Devon", *TGSL*, vol. 3, pt. 1 (1829),
pp. 161-70.
[3] De la Beche, p. 166.   [4] De la Beche, p. 166.

of which is extant as Fascicule B., together with a preface and several short papers. Its style shows that it had not been finally revised for the press. As far as we know, at least twenty-four of the plates were ready to illustrate the fossils, with the memoirs, fascicules E., F., and G., to describe them. Fascicule H., water-marked 1827, is a revision of a portion of B. Eventually MacEnery issued to the public a printed prospectus announcing: "Shortly will be published in one volume Quarto, Cavern Researches." From its wording it seems to be the second notice, and it announces a more elaborate publication than was his first intention to produce. He says: "It has been found necessary to extend the number of the plates to thirty." Original copies of this prospectus are in the Torquay Museum, and they bear a watermark 1828.[1]

According to his manuscript, he was exploring the caves of Chudleigh in August 1829, and he visited another cave in the neighbourhood of Buckfastleigh in December of the same year. These dates are given because they are the last definite

[1] A copy is reproduced in *TDA*, vol. 3 (1869), p. 198.

records of his exploration work that have so far been discovered. At this period, also, it would seem that he was greatly pre-occupied with the question of the flint implements.

A few months later, in April 1830, the poor state of his health compelled him to relinquish his pastoral work at Torquay and to travel abroad. While on the Continent, he visited Paris, saw Cuvier, and presented a collection of organic remains to the Jardin des Plantes; this was the third he had given to that institution. Among the fossils were two portions of a human jaw and some isolated single teeth. These were from a skeleton found in poor condition in a grave inside the entrance of Kent's Cavern. He wrote: "M. Cuvier, to whom I submitted the fragment in 1831, was struck with the form of the jaw. He pronounced it to belong to the Caucasian race." MacEnery is probably referring to this visit to the Continent when he says, "I have identified the flints with ... those especially which are in the British and in the museums of the Jardin des Plantes and Boulogne sur Mer."

On 15 April 1831 he was in Rome and

finally returned home in December to Torquay, where he remained for two and a half years. During this time he was probably at work on fascicules C. and D., which are revisions of his early efforts and contain his studies of flint implements.

According to contemporary accounts, it would appear that he still adhered to his intention of publishing *Cavern Researches*. The *Teignmouth Guide* (second volume, 1832 or 1833) states that Kent's Hole "has been very diligently explored, and we are looking forward with great interest to the publication of a work that has been announced by a gentleman of Torquay, which will contain an account of the treasures that have been unearthed." In another guide-book, *The Panorama of Torquay*, a long descriptive letter on Kent's Cavern dated 16 March 1832, over the signature of Thomas Northmore (with whom MacEnery made his first exploration), gives more definite information:

The Rev. Mr MacEnery ... circulated a prospectus about five years since, of a work then "*shortly to be published in one volume quarto*," entitled "*Cavern Researches or discoveries of organic remains, and of Druidical and Roman Reliques, in the Caves of Kent's Hole, Chudleigh and Berryhead; illustrated with plates, etc., including views, sections and ground plans.*" I regret much that these long-promised works have not yet made their appearance. [Reference is then also made to Buckland's second volume of *Reliquiae Diluvianae.*] For the delay of the Oxonian professor I have heard no reason publicly assigned; but Mr MacEnery has complained, and justly, "of the limited circulation of works of this nature being by no means equal to the expenses", and therefore he has been "obliged to solicit the support of those who may feel an interest in the result of his researches". Hence it is highly probable that his work has been postponed, I hope not suppressed, for want of support.[1]

MacEnery was only a private chaplain, to the Cary family of Tor Abbey, and he possessed no independent means. He therefore sought public support, as no printer would have risked the publication of such

[1] Published in *TDA*, vol. 2 (1867), p. 480.

an expensive scientific work with so limited a circulation. He appears to have appealed twice to the public for subscriptions before he had to abandon his design. Buckland had assisted him by having sixteen out of the thirty large plates lithographed at his own expense; of these fine plates Torquay Museum possesses a series of nineteen. This kindly assistance of Buckland, added to his well-known authority on the subject of cave exploration, seems to have caused some delay in MacEnery's attempts to venture into print: his interpretation of the position of the flints was not in accordance with the views of his older and more experienced colleague. This MacEnery states when speaking of skeletal remains, in Fascicule A., which was written shortly before his death.

An additional reason of postponement was the precarious state of MacEnery's health and his consequent absences from Torquay. For a man of frail constitution and suffering continual ill-health, the five years of fatiguing work he spent digging in a damp underground atmosphere cannot have been beneficial. There is every reason to believe that these labours seriously impaired his health, not to mention three accidents that nearly ended fatally. Speaking of these incidents, he describes how, having crawled down a sewer-like tunnel beneath the stalagmite:

> I had only gone about a hundred paces when owing it is to be feared to foul air my light was extinguished and I was deprived of my senses—my friends supposed me lost and despaired of drawing me out.—I was however extricated by my faithful fellow-labourer Walsh, to whom I am indebted for my life. (I was drawn out in a state of insensibility, and it was not till after some hours' exposure to the air that I recovered.)—I suffered for some weeks from the consequence of imprudence and it was some time before I was able to revisit the cavern.[1]

At another time a globular boulder of spar, five feet in diameter, rolled down into the shaft, thirty feet deep, in which he was working, and he narrowly escaped being crushed to death.

[1] MacEnery, "Cavern Researches", *TDA*, vol. 3 (1869), p. 233.

It is in reference to his ill-health that we have the next definite date of his movements. In a rough draft of the *Collections* of the Rev. George Oliver, a personal friend of his, we read: "From pursuing his Cavern and Geological Researches with excess of ardour, his naturally weak constitution forced him to retire 17 July 1834. For a considerable time he travelled abroad: during his lengthened absence he was much missed."

On 6 November 1837, MacEnery may have been in Paris, for on that date he was elected a member of the Société Géologique de France, on the presentation of M. de Blainville (Cuvier's successor) and M. Brochant de Villiers, professor at the École des Mines. De Blainville, in his *Ostéographie*, frequently cites a "Description of the Cavern of Kent's Hole, Devonshire", which he supposes to have been published by Mr MacEnery, but which he regrets that he has not been able to procure. Probably it was the plates to illustrate his forthcoming work which MacEnery had shown De Blainville.

It would be of interest to know if, during his continental tour, he visited Liége, and became acquainted with Schmerling, who had begun similar explorations four years after the start of his own. Schmerling, likewise, had received very little public encouragement, although Lyell speaks of him as "a skilful anatomist and palaeontologist". He had discovered, in limestone caves in the neighbourhood of Liége, not only flint implements in association with the fossils of extinct animals, but also fossil human remains which were apparently of the same epoch. Lyell examined this collection in 1833 and, unbiased critic that he was, considered the evidence unconvincing for the alleged antiquity of man. Two years later Buckland visited Liége and saw the fossils, but came away incredulous. We who are wise after the event and wonder at the short-sightedness of the experts must, however, bear in mind Lyell's own words of apology in 1863, for his failure to see, years before, the truth of Schmerling's proofs: "A discovery which seems to contradict the general tenor of previous investigations is naturally received with much hesitation.[1]

[1] C. Lyell, *The Geological Evidences of the Antiquity of Man*, London, 1863, p. 68.

MacEnery was absent five years, and returned to England in the spring of 1839. He appears to have at once set about the finishing of his long-delayed publication. One wonders if he was spurred on by the detailed and specialized quartos of Schmerling's *Recherches sur les ossemens fossiles découverts dans les cavernes de la province de Liége* (1833-34), from which he gives several long quotations in his manuscript of this period.

Although MacEnery does not appear to have carried out any further excavations, yet he was no longer a novice in geology and palaeontology. Fascicule A., which by internal evidence shows that it was either written or extensively revised some time after the year 1837, gives much information in an opening passage:

It is at this point that my labours commence of which, though late, I propose to lay the narrative before the public. I had hoped, and it was to be desired, that the subject would have been taken up in the interval by those best able to handle it [no doubt Buckland, who had lectured on Kent's

Cavern in 1835 at Oxford], and it was in this expectation that I had long laid aside all intention of sending my notes to the press. Other and greater undertakings have retarded the execution of the design where I knew it was contemplated. [Buckland was occupied with the long-promised second volume of *Reliquiae Diluvianae*, which he published under another title in 1836.][1]

There remains to me therefore no other alternative than to yield to the duty which my discoveries impose on me, towards science, by publishing an account of what I know of the cavern. I avail myself of the return of health accorded to me by a merciful Providence to record those researches, from which illness not improbably occasioned by them, has long compelled me to desist.[2]

This was perhaps written about 1839-40. In this his last manuscript we have his final opinion about the makers of those

[1] W. Buckland, *Geology and Mineralogy considered with reference to Natural Theology*, London, 1836, 2 vols.

[2] MacEnery, "Cavern Researches", *TDA*, vol. 3 (1869), pp. 207-8.

primitive flint implements, who must have lived "at a great distance from that epoch" of the Celtic burials at the entrance to the cave:

The very circumstance of the diffusion of larger animals and beasts of prey over the surface may have made man collect into communities for his self-defence and protection; and at best his numbers could bear but a small proportion to the races of animals which thickly peopled the forests and plains.

As he was not likely to associate with them, it is vain to look for his remains among theirs—but it is not impossible that his remains may yet be found collected together where whole communities perished by the same catastrophe that overwhelmed the races of elephant, rhinoceros, hyena, tiger and bear. ... M. Schmerling in his turn claims remote antiquity for his human remains found in the cavern of Engis, Liége, and carries it as far back as the epoch of the fossil animals.[1]

[1] MacEnery, pp. 227-9.

This Fascicule A., from which the quotation is taken, and which runs to about a hundred closely-written pages, was probably the last he wrote. It is the most completely written account of his cavern researches and was almost ready for the press, but he never lived to see it in the printer's hands. His new lease of life was illusory; by the autumn of 1840 he was a complete invalid, and the Rev. Charles Fisher was called in to take charge of his pastoral work. To quote the words of his friend, the Rev. George Oliver, "Returning from his travels with no improvement to his health, he led a lingering life and died (quietly in his chair at the Abbey) on Thursday evening, 18 February 1841."[1] He was buried in the churchyard of St Saviour's, Tor; and his gravestone records: "Mr MacEnery was the pioneer of systematic observations in Kent's Hole and the other caverns in the neighbourhood, the sagacious and reverent observer of the works in nature of Him, whose is the earth and the fulness thereof."

[1] George Oliver, *Collections, Illustrating the history of the Catholic religion in the counties of Cornwall, Devon, Dorset, Somerset, Wiltshire and Gloucestershire*, London, 1857, p. 352.

What became of his fine collection of Pleistocene fossils and the many precious manuscripts—about 600 pages—of the investigations of Kent's Hole and other caverns, together with the plates intended for its illustration? They were sold by auction by Mr Nicholas Walke at Webb's Hotel, Torquay, in 1842. A copy of the sale catalogue, published at sixpence, is to be found in the library of the Geological Society of London. It mentions rare fossils, minerals and paintings, but not the manuscripts of his intended work, *Cavern Researches*. These doubtless went astray among miscellaneous papers and portfolios, and were sold for a few shillings. The collection of Pleistocene mammalia, at that day the finest of its kind in England, was scattered in 164 separate lots. Murchison speaks of it in his presidential address to the Geological Society on 18 February 1842:

Mr MacEnery's collection of the bones of British cavern quadrupeds, which is one of high merit, will, I understand, be soon disposed of to the public; and I trust that part of it at least will find a resting place in our great national collection at the British Museum.[1]

Happily the authorities of the British Museum were not backward on this occasion, and made extensive purchases. A dealer present at the sale afterwards remarked, perhaps in disappointment, "Mr Konig, of the British Museum, was the great purchaser at that sale, and might be said to have the nation's purse." It was these specimens that Sir Richard Owen, the famous palaeontogist, employed so excellently in illustrating his *British Fossil Mammals and Birds* (1846), and his appreciation is shown in the acknowledgment:

It is to the assiduous researches of the late Rev. Mr MacEnery that the discovery of the various and interesting fossils of this cave [Kent's Hole] is principally due, and some of the rarest and most valuable of this gentleman's collection have been lately acquired by the British Museum.[2]

[1] *PGSL*, vol. 3 (1834-42), p. 640.
[2] Sir Richard Owen, *A History of British Fossil Mammals and Birds*, London, 1846, p. 103.

Other Investigators Take Up The Research

In many of the modern text books epitomizing the story of the early discoveries of the antiquity of man and of his contemporaneity with extinct mammalia, the part played by MacEnery, William Pengelly and the Torquay Natural History Society is usually condensed to only a paragraph. On the other hand a full measure of praise is meted out to Boucher de Perthes; and it is often forgotten that it was the spadework of these English pioneers which induced Falconer, Prestwich and Evans to take up the cause of the famous and versatile archaeologist of Abbeville. An attempt therefore will be made to relate in their proper order the series of events that led up to the revolution of scientific opinion in 1859 on the antiquity of the human species. These, when seen in their true sequence, from Kent's Cavern to the valley of the Somme, are also the vindication of MacEnery's discoveries.

As early as 25 March 1840, R. A. C. Godwin-Austen read a paper to the Geological Society of London entitled, "On

the Bone Caves of Devonshire".[1] Strange
to say, in the published account, there is
no mention of human fossil bones. Godwin-
Austen elaborated a theory of how powerful felines and not hyenas had dragged into
the caves the various animals of which the
fossil bones were found. Buckland was in
the chair, and afterwards made playful
criticisms only of this theory; for he
"backed the hyenas". A year later Godwin-
Austen and Buckland had "an interesting
discussion" at the Plymouth meeting of
the British Association. A paper had been
read on the Pleistocene deposits of Devon
and Cornwall. Relative to what had been
said about the deposits in Ash Hole,
Berryhead:

> Mr Austen observed, that the occur-
> rence of human remains and works of
> art associated with the elephant and
> other bones at Ash Hole, confirmed the
> opinion he entertained of their con-
> temporaneity. At Kent's Hole, near
> Torquay, arrows and knives of flint, with
> human bones, in the same condition as
> the elephant and other bones, were

[1] *PGSL*, vol. 3 (1838-42), pp. 286-7.

found in an undisturbed bed of clay,
covered by nine feet of stalagmite. ...

Dr Buckland contended that human
remains had never been found under
such circumstances as to prove their
contemporaneous existence with the
hyenas and bears of the caverns. In
Kent's Hole, the Celtic knives and
human bones were found in holes *dug by
art*, and which had disturbed the floor of
the cave and the bones below it. ... He
also gave an amusing account of a cave
in Wales [Paviland], in which he had
found the skeleton of a female who had
been buried among fossil remains, and
who had evidently kept a sort of sutler's
shop as appeared from the remains of
Celtic implements of gambling, and
other amusements of a camp.[1]

This discussion is not mentioned in the
Official Report of the Association but is to
be found in the *Athenaeum* and *Literary
Gazette* for 14 August 1841. Since then
time has shown that Buckland's views on
the skeletal remains (but not the flints)

[1] *TGSL*, second series, vol. 6, pt. 2, pp. 433-89.

were correct for Kent's Cavern but in error as regards Paviland Cave.

In 1842, the Geological Society published a memoir by Godwin-Austen entitled "On the Geology of the South-east of Devonshire". It is a synthesis of five papers written between 1834 to 1840. In the final portion, the author stated, from personal investigation in Kent's Cavern, two definite facts:

The bones and works of man [flint implements] must have been introduced into the cave before the flooring of stalagmite had been formed.[1]

And, secondly:

Human remains and works of art, such as arrow-heads and knives of flint, occur in all parts of the cave and throughout the entire thickness of the clay ... [beneath the stalagmite]: and no distinction founded on condition, distribution or relative position can be observed

[1] R. A. C. Godwin-Austen, "On the Geology of the South-east of Devonshire", *TGSL*, second series, vol. 6, pt. 2, p. 446.

whereby the human can be separated from the other reliquiae.[1]

In other words, he declared that, as far as the evidence showed, there was no reason to separate man from the period of the extinct fauna.

Unfortunately the value of Godwin-Austen's evidence on the co-existence of the fabricators of the flint tools and the extinct animals was weakened by the statement about human bones. To Buckland, who, through his associations with MacEnery, was well acquainted with the Cavern, it must have seemed very questionable whether this statement was true. The wording of the memoir certainly implies that human remains occurred with the flints and extinct fauna:

Few, I imagine, who are acquainted with the facts which the labours of MM. Schmerling, Marcel de Serres, and others have established, entertain any doubt as to the fact that the bones of man have been found in caves; what I wish to state distinctly is, that they

[1] Godwin-Austen, p. 444.

occur in Kent's Cave under precisely the same conditions as the bones of all the other animals. The value of such a statement must rest on the care with which a collector may have explored; I must therefore state that my own researches were constantly conducted in parts of the cave which had never been disturbed, and in every instance the bones were procured from beneath a thick covering of stalagmite; so far then, the bones and works of man must have been introduced into the cave before the flooring of stalagmite had been formed. It may be suggested, that this cave was used as a place of sepulture by some early inhabitants of this country, and the bones of the animals occupied the lower parts of the cave when such sepulture took place. ...[1] There is not a single appearance which can suggest that the cave has been used as a place of sepulture.[2]

MacEnery, nevertheless, had found several such burials which he recognized were of a later period. But he had never

[1] Godwin-Austen, p. 446.   [2] Godwin-Austen, p. 444.

discovered among the bones of the extinct fauna any human bones—not even a single tooth. In the later excavations conducted by members of the British Association (1865-80), it was only after three years of work that they came across a portion of an upper jaw with four teeth; and this was all they ever found in fifteen years of excavations.

Nothing of the kind was afterwards found either in or beneath the stalagmite. The discoverers, from the condition of the relic, were disposed to assign it to a date more recent than that of the palaeolithic implements.[1]

But the subject was not allowed to pass into oblivion. The Torquay Natural History Society, in the enthusiasm of its first year, deputed two of its members (on 8 Sept. 1845) "to wait on Sir Lawrence Palk requesting permission to explore Kent's Hole for the purpose of obtaining fossil remains" for their museum. In the

[1] H. Pengelly (ed.), *A Memoir of William Pengelly of Torquay, geologist, with a selection of his correspondence*, London, 1897, p. 307.

following summer the project was publicly announced, with the further intention "to ascertain whether the flint knives and relics of human art which appear to have been found intermixed with the fossil bones of extinct animals, are really contemporary with them". That the question aroused some interest in the town is evident from some amusing verses contributed to the local newspaper.[1]

William Pengelly was one of three appointed to superintend the explorations. The hopes of the Society were realized. Out of five flint implements that they discovered, two were unmistakably beneath the virgin stalagmite and lay among fossil teeth of cave hyenas and fragments of bone which evidently had been their prey: the other three were in soil that had been moved by previous explorers. A report was published in *The Torquay and Tor Directory* (6 Nov. 1846) stating the essential premises and leaving the conclusion open, but clearly intimated:

Whatever theory may be founded upon these most interesting discoveries, which

[1] Some are cited in *TDA*, vol. 10, pp. 161-2.

are so much at variance with the
opinions generally entertained by geologists in regard to the comparative
antiquity of human relics, and the
remains of extinct animals,—of the fact
itself there cannot be a question. It is a
satisfactory confirmation of this opinion
that Mr McEnery had arrived at the
same conclusion, as is evident from
several passages in his unpublished
memoir.[1]

On 12th May the following year Mr
Edward Vivian read an account of these
researches to the Geological Society; and
although he went only so far as to conclude
that man inhabited Kent's Cavern, perhaps subsequent to its occupation by the
extinct non-human mammals and certainly prior to the formation of the stalagmite, yet the Society's published extract of
the paper[2] carefully omitted the vexed
question of the flint implements. To quote
Vivian's own words, "The paper was considered so heterodox that its insertion in
the *Transactions* was delayed until the late

[1] *TDA*, vol. 10, pp. 164-5.
[2] Reported in the *Athenaeum*, 5 June 1847.

lamented Dr Buckland could again visit the cavern, which he was never able to accomplish."[1] A month later, at the 1847 meeting of the British Association at Oxford, a letter from Vivian, on the same subject, was read to the Geological Section —Buckland was the president—and a synopsis was printed in the reports. It was confined to stating: "The important point that we have established is that relics of human art are found *beneath* the unbroken floor of stalagmite."[2]

It is noteworthy that about this time Boucher de Perthes published the first of his three volumes: *Antiquités celtiques et antédiluviennes. Mémoire sur l'industrie primitive et les arts à leur origine* (Paris, 1847-9). The preface begins by referring to his earlier work *De la Création* (Paris, 1838-41, 5 vols.) in which the hope was expressed that sooner or later fossil skeletons and other "traces" of antediluvian man would be found.

With this conviction, Boucher de Perthes, for the next ten years, spared

[1] The Council and Officers of the Geological Society included De la Beche (in the chair), Lyell, Owen, Sedgwick, Forbes, Falconer, Murchison and Darwin, but not Buckland.

[2] *Report of the 17th Meeting of the British Association for the Advancement of Science*, 1847, p. 73.

neither time nor money in the search for
material proof of his theory. He supervised
innumerable excavations in the valleys of
the Somme and the Seine; he investigated
gravel pits; he kept an eye on new cuttings
for roads, railways and fortifications.
Although he found no fossil bones of antediluvian man, yet he found an enormous
quantity of his handiwork. He states that
this "débris" was among the fossil bones
of elephant, mastodons and saurians, and
very often found at a considerable depth.
He claimed to have unearthed "des armes,
des utensils, des figures, des signes, des
symboles", all in stone. Wherever fossil
bones of animals were found, careful
search, he felt sure, would bring to light
"ces mêmes ébauches de l'industrie humaine".

He further claimed these "traces" revealed the arts, religion, symbolic signs
and hieroglyphic language of antediluvian
man. He had even found small models in
flint of dolmens and Druidic standing
stones.

The book is a fine octavo volume, well
printed, containing 500 pages of text and
125 pages of notes and correspondence,

with 80 plates comprising 1600 figures. Unfortunately, Boucher de Perthes, in his enthusiasm, discovered far too much of his antediluvian man. Although there are some plates of undoubted Palaeolithic axes, yet the majority of the plates figure flints which are merely freaks of nature. He declared, "These rude stones prove the existence of man as surely as a whole Louvre would have done".

As N. Joly said, "the heated imagination of the antiquary, unconsciously influenced by a deceitful illusion, discovered on flints the figures of men, of animals, of plants, carved with a definite intention, and even graphic signs, true hieroglyphs." These discoveries and the man himself, the French geologists treated with contemptuous scepticism.[1]

There were, of course, some exceptions. Among them was Dr Rigollot, who had at first strenuously opposed the theories of Boucher de Perthes. But when seeking evidence to disprove them, he himself unearthed flint axes in the sand pits of St Acheul and was converted. His interesting paper, *Mémoire sur des instruments en silex*

[1] N. Joly, *Man Before Metals*, London, 1885.

trouvés à Saint-Acheul (1854) was discussed by the Geological Society of France in January 1855 and discounted.

Lady Prestwich, in her "Recollections of M. Boucher de Perthes" (1895),[1] throws interesting sidelights on the Abbeville antiquarian. He was a vigorous old gentleman of seventy when she met him in 1858. His was a versatile pen, and he wrote books of his travels in countries from Russia to Scotland and Ireland, light literature, plays, romances and ballads as well as serious antiquarian works. She says: "He was notorious for having previously propounded theories regarding the antiquity of man without any facts to support them; therefore it was not surprising that, when he hit upon a great discovery, he could not obtain a hearing and was treated as a wild visionary."[2] The writer is doubtless repeating current gossip of what the French were saying afterwards by way of excuse. The undaunted old gentleman never ceased to persevere in the fight for what he believed was the truth. His second volume, with

---

[1] Published in her *Essays Descriptive and Biographical*, London, 1901.
[2] Grace Prestwich, *Essays*, p. 79.

508 pages and 26 plates, appeared in 1857, and the third in 1864, with 678 pages and 12 plates.

Another interesting event about this time was the chance discovery of the lost manuscript of MacEnery. In 1842 a tradesman of Torquay, interested in Devonian fossils, had purchased at the sale of MacEnery's effects a lot consisting of loose papers and other "odds and ends"; among them was the valuable manuscript. After extracts from it had been published by Vivian in the *Torquay Directory*, it passed by purchase to Mr W. Long, F.G.S., who presented it to Vivian with a view to its publication.

This voluminous manuscript, now in Torquay Museum, may be divided into ten fascicules, and consists "of separate narratives or essays, in which the Cavern and the discoveries made in it are described, and their bearing on Palaeontology, Archaeology, Anthropology and Theology are discussed". It is probable that there were originally some 600 written pages, of which about 400 survive. This was the principal source of Vivian's lectures, which did so much to familiarize the public mind with the claims of Kent's Cavern.

In 1856 Vivian brought the manuscript to the notice of the British Association assembled at Cheltenham by reading two papers. The first is entitled: "Researches in Kent's Cavern, Torquay, with the original MS. memoir of its first opening, by the late Rev. J. MacEnery (long supposed to have been lost) and the Report of the Sub-Committee of the Torquay Natural History Society."[1] This paper is printed in full in the report and contains interesting extracts descriptive of MacEnery's work in the cavern.

The second paper is entitled "On the earliest traces of Human Remains in Kent's Cavern."[2] In it Vivian appears to have been very chary in what he said:

The position of the flint instruments beneath the stalagmite, although contrary to the generally received opinion of geologists, and carrying back the first occupation of Devon to very high

[1] *Report of the British Association*, Cheltenham, 1856, pp. 78-80.
[2] *Report of the British Association*, Cheltenham, 1856, pp. 119-22.

antiquity, was shown to be not necessarily at variance with Scriptural chronology. ...

The sources from which the statements in the paper were obtained were principally the original manuscript memoir of the late Rev. J. MacEnery, F.G.S., which is deplored by Professor Owen in his *Fossil Mammalia*, and by other writers, as lost to science, but which had been recovered by Mr [Edward] Vivian and was produced before the Section; also the report of the subcommittee of the Torquay Natural History Society, and his own researches.[1]

THE ANTIQUITY OF MAN IS PROVED

For a dozen years (1846-58) the lectures of Vivian and Pengelly on Kent's Cavern did excellent propaganda work by affording matter and occasion for discussion and controversy. Towards the close of the

[1] E. Vivian, "On the Earliest Traces of Human Remains in Kent's Cavern", *Report of the British Association*, Cheltenham, 1856, pp. 119-22.

period, the reward of this persistent work came at last. In January 1858, during the absence of the workmen quarrying limestone on the slope of Windmill Hill, above the fishing town of Brixham, some practical joker thrust one of their boring tools down a fissure in the rock. In recovering the tool a cave was discovered, with a fine reindeer antler partly embedded in the stalagmite floor, and giving every evidence of containing other fossil bones. As no human hand had ransacked these treasures since the time the stalagmite had sealed them up ages before, here was very possibly an ideal opportunity of settling by scientific investigation the vexed question as to what were the exact conditions in which the remains of the extinct fauna and the flint implements really occurred. The secretary of the Torquay Natural History Society, William Pengelly, hastened to secure a lease of the cave before its precious contents could be interfered with; but the proprietor asking too high a price, the project seemed likely to be abandoned.

Fortunately Dr Hugh Falconer, who was touring the cave districts of the

Mendips, Devon and South Wales, while visiting Kent's Cavern, heard of the discovery of the new cave at Brixham. "Singularly skilful in discriminating fossil mammalia, and well accustomed both in India and Europe to enquire into their geological distribution", he and the indefatigable Pengelly joined forces and lost no time in taking full advantage of this rare occasion. On 10 May 1858 Falconer wrote a long and urgent letter to the Geological Society of London, pointing out the unique opportunity and pressing them to take the matter up:

> Taking into account the vast richness of Kent's Hole in fossil remains, the dispersion of Mr McEnery's collections, and the grievous fate of the MS. labours of about twenty years of his life, it is submitted to the Council whether there is not a prospect of equal wealth in this promising and adjoining cave of Brixham, and whether the case is not one deserving of a combined effort among Geologists to organize operations for having it satisfactorily explored, before mischief is done by

untutored zeal and desultory work.[1]
[He tactfully avoided the question of
the antiquity of man.]

This letter, urging the opportunity of
working out completely a virgin bone-
cavern, resulted in the famous Brixham
Cave explorations (July 1858-June 25
1859) under the auspices of the Royal and
Geological Societies, and under the watch-
ful eyes of the foremost geologists and
palaeontologists of the day. To Falconer
was entrusted the laying down of the plan
of operations, while to Pengelly fell the
important task of superintending the excavations.

The smallness of the cave permitted
them to adopt a very exact and sure
method of work. Instead of digging trial
pits through the stalagmite and cave
earth, the contents were bodily removed in
sections, layer by layer, like sheets of
paper. In this way fossils and flints were
revealed in their proper horizon, and all
danger of mingling and confusing objects
of different levels was prevented. The

[1] H. Falconer, *Palaeontological memoirs and notes. With a biographical sketch of the author*, ed. C. Murchison, London, 1868,
vol. 2, p. 489.

scrupulous care with which the investigations were carried out, and the names of the members of the Committee entrusted with the task, were a guarantee of the genuineness of the results.

In September, the work had so far advanced that a signed "Report of Progress in the Brixham Cave" was forwarded by Falconer, A. C. Ramsay and Pengelly, to the General Committee and laid before the Royal Society. It stated:

Several well-marked specimens of the objects called "Flint Knives", and generally accepted at the present day as the early products of rude Keltic or pre-Keltic industry, have been exhumed from different parts of the cavern, mixed in the ochreous earth indiscriminately with remains of *Rhinoceros*, *Hyena*, and other extinct forms. ... We failed in detecting evidence that these so-called "Flint Knives" were of a different age, as regards the period of their introduction, from the bones of the extinct animals occurring in the same stratum of cave-earth, or that they were introduced into the cavern by different

agencies. ... It may be anticipated that
data will be arrived at for settling the
disputed question of the contemporaneous introduction, or otherwise, of the
supposed human industrial objects into
the cavern along with the remains of
the extinct Mammalia.[1]

This report was read by Ramsay at the
Leeds meeting of the British Association;
and Pengelly contributed a paper, "On a
recently-discovered Ossiferous Cavern at
Brixham, nr. Torquay". He described the
structure and formation of the cavern and
how it was excavated. In the discussion
that followed, the President, Owen, "said
he was glad that means had been taken
for the careful exploration of this cave",
but "it would be premature to raise any
hypothesis until the whole of the facts were
before them ... and he should refrain,
therefore, from expressing any opinion,
but he wished to caution them against
coming to conclusions as to the antiquity
of these remains ..." He then proceeded
to show with some ingenuity how it might
have been possible for some of these now

[1] Falconer, vol. 2, pp. 495-6.

extinct animals to have existed right down to the dawn of the historic period; and concluded by stating "he should be very glad to see a good fossil human being" before he changed his opinion.[1]

It is only fair to quote here a private letter written previously to Falconer by Prestwich, a member of the general committee of the Brixham Cavern explorations, and dated 21 Sept.:

I have to-day read the report ... for my own part I should not like to have it read at the Brit. Assoc. ... Now, although you have so good a case with regard to occurrence and position of the worked flints, I yet hesitate to accept the conclusions, and many others will probably do the same. There may be possibilities of mistake which further workings may serve to correct, or, on the other hand further workings may bring to light other facts tending to prove indisputably the remarkable association you allude to.

I quite agree with you that there is now much evidence tending in the

[1] *Athenaeum*, 9 Oct. 1858.

same direction—so much that there is hope that, if true, it may receive some unmistakable corroboration: but until we have that, and that I have myself *worked* on the ground and looked at all the bearings, I hesitate and wait.[1]

This cautious attitude of Owen and Prestwich may explain the reason for not publishing either the signed report or Pengelly's paper in the British Association's Annual Report.

But within a few months new evidence was exposed which proved that Falconer, Ramsay and Pengelly, the actual workers in the Brixham Cavern, were correct in their conclusions. Ill health and the prospects of an English winter had driven Falconer, in October, to France and the south, on his way to Sicily. He visited all localities of geological interest. He called at Abbeville to examine Boucher de Perthes' immense collection of so-called worked flints, many of which he claimed to have dug up with his own hands in the river gravels of the Somme valley, mixed

[1] Grace Prestwich, *Life and Letters of Sir Joseph Prestwich*, Edinburgh, 1899, p. 117.

indiscriminately with the molars of the mammoth. As we know, French scientists had laughed at his collections and made sport of his theories, but it was otherwise with Falconer. He at once (1 Nov. 1858) wrote to Prestwich strongly recommending him to visit Abbeville:

> After devoting the greater part of a day to his vast collection, I am perfectly satisfied that there is a great deal of fair presumptive evidence in favour of many of his speculations regarding the remote antiquity of these industrial objects, and their association with animals now extinct. Monsieur Boucher's hotel is, from ground-floor to garret, a continued museum filled with pictures, medieval art, and Gaulish antiquities, including antediluvian flint-knives, fossil bones etc. ... Boucher de Perthes is a very courteous elderly French gentleman. ... What I have seen here gives me still greater impulse to persevere in our Brixham exploration.[1]

Prestwich, in reply, promised to visit the

[1] Grace Prestwich, *Life and Letters*, pp. 119-20.

locality at an early opportunity and make the acquaintance of Boucher de Perthes. His letter, dated 4 Feb. 1859, reveals to us that he was gradually acquiescing in the conclusions of Falconer and Pengelly:

Austen is satisfied that the flint implements occur with the bones. After my last visit [to Brixham] I cannot deny it, but still I am not satisfied without seeking every other possible explanation besides that of contemporaneous existence. None of the evidence which has come before me during the last ten years has appeared to me conclusive, and now we have an opportunity of settling the question more satisfactorily we cannot be too cautious.[1]

There was not another man in England whose knowledge of the Quaternary sands and gravels equalled that of Prestwich. It was humorously said of him: "Point out a broken pebble amongst a thousand others in a gravel pit, and there is one who will tell you the point of the compass from

[1] Grace Prestwich, *Life and Letters*, p. 120.

which it came, the stratum which yielded it, the distance it has travelled, the amount of rolling it has undergone, and the time it has occupied in the journey." His authority on the other side of the Channel was also well recognized. Part of his education had been in Paris, and he wrote and spoke French fluently. Further, he was well acquainted with the geology of France and with her leading geologists, and had read papers before their societies.

April 1859 saw Prestwich on his memorable visit to the valley of the Somme in company with England's expert on stone implements, Sir John Evans. A second visit was made with Godwin-Austen and the anatomist, Wickham Flower. A few days later he went over the ground at Amiens with Lyell. Here was evidence he could expertly evaluate: clear sections, in gravel-pits, of undisturbed strata, seen in broad daylight, not excavations in a murky cavern by torchlight. Instead of weeks of claustrophobic investigations in underground passages, a few afternoon inspections by such an expert as Prestwich would solve the problem of the exact relations of the flint implements and the extinct animals. He accepted no evidence except that which he himself had personally investigated.

The result was that on 26 May 1859, only one month after his first visit, Prestwich startled the scientific world with his classic memoir read to the Royal Society: "On the Occurrence of Flint Implements, associated with the Remains of Extinct Mammalia, in Undisturbed Beds of a late Geological Period."[1]

In this paper Prestwich cautiously refrained from pronouncing dogmatically on the antiquity of man, and contented himself with demonstrating man's contemporaneity with certain extinct forms of elephant, rhinoceros, deer and other animals. He was inclined not so much to throw the human period backward as to bring down the period of the extinct mammalia nearer to historic time. Three years later, however, in his memoir in 1862, he gave it as his opinion that the accumulating weight of evidence compelled us to extend greatly

[1] The paper, which was read on 26 May 1859, was published in the *Philosophical Transactions* of 1860, and printed in 1861 as "On the Occurrence of Flint Implements, associated with the remains of extinct mammalia, in undisturbed beds of a late geological period in France, at Amiens and Abbeville, and in England at Hoxne", *PTRS*, 1861, pp. 277-316.

our present chronology with regard to the first existence of man.

The revival of the study of prehistoric man was general, not only in this country, but also on the Continent. Its success abroad was in great measure due to another memoir that Prestwich forwarded to the French Academy of Sciences, "Sur la découverte d'instruments en silex associés à des Restes de Mammifères, d'Espèces perdues dans des Couches non-remaniées d'une Formation géologique récente."[1] One immediate result of this paper was that Prestwich's friend, M. Albert Gaudy,

... visited Abbeville and Amiens to examine the implements and the flint-bearing beds. He found worked flints *in situ*, and his researches confirmed M. de Perthes' statements; his report had the effect in Paris that the paper to the Royal Society had in England, and a French pilgrimage to the valley of the Somme began, headed by well-known members of the Institute, among whom

[1] Published in the *Comptes-rendus* for 1859.

were MM. de Quatrefages, Lartet, Hébert and many others.[1]

There can be no doubt that it was the famous memoir of Prestwich which revolutionized scientific opinion on the antiquity of man; other papers gave further aid in bringing the subject before the public—for example, that given on 2 June 1859 to the Society of Antiquaries: "On the occurrence of Flint Implements in undisturbed Beds of Gravel, Sand and Clay (such as are known by Geologists under the name of Drift) in several localities, both on the Continent and this Country", by John Evans.[2] On 22 June, the Geological Society called an extraordinary meeting for which the programme was, "Further observations on the occurrence of Objects of Human Art in the Bone-Breccia of the Caves near Palermo", by Dr Falconer; "Report on the Progress of the Explorations of the Cave at Brixham", by J. Prestwich; "On a Flint-Implement recently obtained from the Gravel near Amiens", by W. Flower.

[1] Grace Prestwich, *Life and Letters*, p. 134.
[2] *AE*, vol. 38 (1860), pp. 289-292.

Prestwich, in his memoir, confessed how much he owed to the stimulating impulse of the Brixham Cave explorations:

It was not until I had myself witnessed the conditions under which flint implements had been found at Brixham that I became fully impressed with the validity of the doubts thrown upon the previously prevailing opinions with respect to such remains in caves.

In his introductory remarks he reviewed the earlier history of the many pioneers who had investigated the vexed question of the cavern deposits. He singled out Schmerling and MacEnery, whose work, he considered, should have merited better treatment, and of both he gave a fair presentation. In proof of this encomium, Vivian had published an abridged edition of MacEnery's *Cavern Researches*, with seventeen of the original plates, one of which figured flint implements of a type similar to those found at Abbeville. More was done, ten years later, when Pengelly brought out a complete edition of the whole manuscript in the *Transac-*

tions of the Devonshire Association for 1869.

One cannot but regret that MacEnery was unable, for want of support, to publish his monograph on Kent's Cavern. Although there exist so many pages of his manuscript, yet these are but the withered leaves of a once fruitful work. In them are disclosed many acute and careful observations on fossil mammalia, flint implements and cave exploration. Besides the loss of the useful assistance of his wealth of knowledge to the scientific world of his day, much also has been lost to us that might otherwise have been more fully recorded by the exigencies of seeing his manuscript through the press. Nevertheless, recalling the scepticism with which Schmerling's excellent quartos were received, it is doubtful, even if Kent's Cavern had been completely described in print, that Brixham Cave and the Somme Valley would have been less celebrated.

When we unravel the tangled influences that were instrumental in bringing about the world's recognition of Palaeolithic man, and trace them back to their original sources, we must admit that the discoveries of Kent's Cavern and its controversies kept the question alive and led up to the opening of Brixham Cave. The value of this second stage of the enquiry lies in the trustworthiness of its evidence. It was the first unransacked ossiferous cavern to be worked out in a completely systematic manner; the first to afford strong *prima facie* evidence; it removed the barrier of doubt. These two caves were the fingerposts of the ultimate road to certainty. Public acceptance of man's being the contemporary of the mammoth and its associates was wrought, not by the discovery of his fossil bones, but by the works of his hands. The gravel pits of the Somme clinched the argument, and Boucher de Perthes leapt into fame.

Falconer wrote on 4 Nov. 1859:

My dear Prestwich, I have a charming letter from M. Boucher de Perthes, full of gratitude to "perfide Albion" for helping him to assured immortality, and giving him a lift when his countrymen of the Institute left him in the gutter. He radiates a benignant smile from his lofty pinnacle on you and me. ...[1]

[1] Grace Prestwich, *Life and Letters*, p. 141.

Abbeville, in 1908, honoured him with a public statue. But William Pengelly should not be forgotten. He rescued MacEnery from oblivion and indefatigably did the spade work, in every sense of the word, which finally induced others to bring the problem to a successful solution.

In Defence of Dr Buckland and Others

This short account of the pioneers of prehistory, from an English point of view, would be incomplete unless some comment were made on the charges which, nowadays, are levelled against those who, before 1859, were reluctant to accept the proofs of man's geological antiquity.

In the case of the neglect of Boucher de Perthes, we have a fair statement of the facts by Professor T. H. Huxley, shortly after the former's death, in his presidential address to the Geological Society, 1869:

The geologists of his own country treated M. Boucher de Perthes's work [*Antiquités celtiques et antédiluviennes*, 1847-9] with indifference and neglect; and no doubt popular historians of science, judging after the event, will hereafter visit them with reprobation for their blindness and their prejudices. But just and critical students of the "Antiquités" will, I think, be able completely to comprehend, and largely to justify, the course taken by the French geologists. Columbus discovered the new world; and great is his fame for that achievement, history, like some other great powers, always paying upon results: but those who will look carefully into the matter will find that most of his reasons for believing in the existence of the new land which he discovered were either insufficient or erroneous, and might well fail to carry conviction to the minds of the much abused kings and ministers who so long withheld their help to his great enterprise.

And I venture to doubt whether, if any cautious person were now to read the *Antiquités Celtiques*, he would rise from its perusal with the feeling that the author's case had been even approximately made out—whether, perhaps, he would not rather be prejudiced against it. Eminently generous, truthful, hearty, and enthusiastic, Boucher de Perthes paid for these virtues, by a certain facility of belief, which is as terrible a drawback to scientific weight as it is advantageous in the struggle against neglect and adverse criticism when a man happens to have laid hold of a truth. I say this much in justification of our *confrères* across the channel, and in vindication of caution and scientific logic, with which I, for one, prefer to err, rather than to be right in the company of haste and guesswork. Posterity, a somewhat short-sighted personage, who, as I have said, pays only upon results, will take no notice of the protest, and will not only reward to our Columbus all the credit which he deserves for being substantially in the right, but will probably abuse those of his contemporaries who were equally in the right for disbelieving him.[1]

How true are Huxley's words with regard to posterity's opinions concerning

[1] *JGSL*, vol. 25 (1869), pp. xxx-xxxi.

Buckland! First of all, it is often forgotten
that the problem for him was not so much
a question of the antiquity of man, but
rather the question whether man had
existed in Europe before the Deluge.
Buckland and Cuvier believed that the
mammoth, the rhinoceros, the cave bear,
of which fossil remains were found in
caverns, had become extinct by the action
of a universal deluge. For Buckland it was
the Noachian, and for Cuvier the one
preceding it. MacEnery says in his manuscript: "Admitting that it was fully established that instruments of art [artefacts]
occur in the midst of the bones [of extinct
species] in places to which we see not how
they could have arrived by any post-
diluvian operation, Dr Buckland considers such a fact would go to supply a link
in the chain of evidence which has been
hitherto a desideratum of no small magni-
tude, namely that man in a savage state
inhabited England before the Deluge."[1]

When the famous passage is quoted
from Cuvier's *Discours sur les révolutions de la
surface du globe*—"Tout porte à croire que

[1] MacEnery, "Cavern Researches", *TDA*, vol. 3 (1869),
p. 332.

l'espèce humaine n'existait point dans les pays où se découvrent les ossements fossiles"—this is taken to mean that Cuvier definitely pronounced against man's being contemporaneous with extinct animals. But to understand what he actually said the whole passage should be read; viz., "All these tend to confirm the assertion, that the human race did not exist in the countries where fossil bones are found, at the epoch of the revolutions which buried these bones; for there cannot be assigned any reason why mankind should have escaped such overwhelming catastrophes, nor why human remains should not now be discovered as well as those of other animals; but I do not wish to conclude that man did not exist previously to this epoch".[1]

The most common assertion, however, against Buckland is that, although he was a first-class geologist and could not miss discovering the traces of early man, yet he was unable to accept the evidence of his own eyes: and this because he was blinded by a cardinal article of belief, based on Holy Writ, that the world had been

[1] The version is that of the English translation of 1829.

created 6000 years ago. "What a pest this fixed idea becomes when a good observer puts this blinker over his eyes!" This accusation, so often repeated, demands a full refutation in Buckland's own words. He writes in the second chapter of *Geology and Mineralogy considered with reference to Natural Theology*:

It may seem just a matter of surprise, that many learned and religious men ... should receive with distrust, or total incredulity, the announcement of conclusions, which the geologist deduces from careful and patient investigation of the facts which it is his province to explore. These doubts and difficulties result from the disclosures made by geology, respecting the lapse of very long periods of time, before the creation of man. Minds which have been long accustomed to date the origin of the universe, as well as that of the human race, from an era of about six thousand years ago, receive reluctantly any information, which if true, demands some modification of their present ideas of cosmogony. ... No reasonable man can doubt that all the phenomena of the natural world derive their origin from God ... and the reluctance with which evidences ... have been admitted by many persons, who are sincerely zealous for the interests of religion, can only be explained by their want of accurate information in physical science. ...

The truth is, that all observers, however various may be their speculations, respecting the secondary causes by which geological phenomena have been brought about, are now agreed in admitting the lapse of very long periods of time to have been an essential condition to the production of these phenomena. ...After all, it should be recollected that the question is not respecting the correctness of the Mosaic narrative, but of our interpretation of it.[1]

In one particular case, that of Paviland Cave, it is said Buckland did not accept the evidence because, as he frankly informs us in his *Geology and Mineralogy*, of "the great difficulty in reconciling the early and

[1] W. Buckland, *Geology and Mineralogy considered with reference to Natural Theology*, London, 1836, vol. i, pp. 8-33.

extended periods which have been assigned
to the extinct races of animals with our
received chronology".[1] To what extended
periods and races of animals was he referring? Was he referring only to that of the
mammoth and other species known to him
as the Diluvium (Pleistocene) or was he
referring to the entire series of geological
formations, viz., what in his day were
known as the Primary, the Secondary and
the Tertiary?

The quotation comes from the eleventh
chapter, "On Supposed Cases of Fossil
Human Bones".

Before we enter on the consideration
of the fossil remains of other animals, it
may be right to enquire whether any
traces of the human species have yet
been found in the strata of the earth.
The only evidence that has yet been
collected upon this subject is negative;
but as far as this extends, no conclusion
is more fully established, than the important fact of the total absence of any
vestiges of the human species throughout the entire series of geological forma-

[1] Buckland, *Geology and Mineralogy*, p.103.

tions. Had the case been otherwise, there would indeed have been great difficulty in reconciling the early and extended periods which have been assigned to the extinct races of animals with our received chronology.[1]

He supports this statement with a reference to Lyell's *Principles of Geology*, which reads, "If there be a difference of opinion respecting the occurrence in certain deposits of the remains of man and his works, it is always in reference to strata confessedly of the most modern order; and it is never pretended that our race co-existed with assemblages of animals and plants of which all the species are extinct."[2]

It is after this statement that Buckland proceeds to discuss the occasional discovery of human bones and works of art in the Pleistocene in conjunction with remains of its extinct animals. His line of reasoning for doubting the evidence of these claims is practically the same as that of Lyell: the lack of cogent and define proof that the proximity of these fossil remains was not

[1] *Geology and Mineralogy*, p. 103.
[2] Vol. 1, pp. 153-4.

due to a commingling of different deposits.

Is it fair to say it was "the clerical bias of Buckland that retarded the march of truth", while for Lyell it was the caution of the geologist over the difficulties of the evidence?

Lyell writes in his *Principles of Geology:*

Must we infer that man and these extinct quadrupeds were contemporaneous inhabitants of the south of France at some former epoch? We should unquestionably have arrived at this conclusion if the bones had been found in an undisturbed *stratified* deposit. ... But we must hesitate before we draw analogous inferences from evidence so equivocal as that afforded by the mud, stalagmites, and breccias of caves where the signs of *successive* depositions are wanting. ...

No one will maintain that man, the hyena, and the bear, were at once joint tenants of these caverns; and if it be necessary to assume that the mud and pebbles were washed into their present position by floods, the same inundations might possibly have caught up the bones

lying in more ancient deposits, and thus
have mingled the whole together in the
same mass.

More than ordinary caution is re-
quired in reasoning on the occurrence of
human remains and works of art in
alluvial deposits, since the chances of
error are much greater than when we
have the fossil bones of the inferior
animals only under consideration. For
the floor of caves has usually been disturbed by the aboriginal inhabitants of
each country, who have used such
retreats for dwelling places, or for con-
cealment, or sepulture. ...

To decide whether certain relics have
been introduced by man, or natural
causes, into masses of transported material, must almost always be a task of
some difficulty. ...

It is not on such evidence that we
shall readily be induced to admit either
the high antiquity of the human race,
or the recent date of certain lost species
of quadrupeds.[1]

It is remarkable that after Lyell had

[1] Vol. 2, pp. 225-7.

again visited most of the localities, his
entirely revised ninth edition of the *Principles of Geology* (1853) goes into fuller
details and reiterates the same difficulties
which complicated the problem. Even
Prestwich affirmed that none of the evidence which had come before him during
that last ten years had appeared to him
conclusive. In the end Lyell was right: it
was not these doubtful fossil bones but the
flint implements that solved the problem.

If we wish to catch a glimpse of the true
Buckland, then there is no need to apolo-
gize for presuming to end with a long
quotation from an inaugural lecture on
"The Influences of Oxford on Geology",
given by W. J. Sollas when he became
Professor of Geology in the University of
Oxford in the year 1897.[1] He gives a true
picture of the illustrious dean who in 1819
was the first to occupy the Chair.

The period of Buckland has been
styled, and justly styled, the "Golden
Age of Geology". Sedgwick was his

[1] Published in *The Age of the Earth, and other geological
studies*, London, 1905, pp. 219-56.

contemporary in Cambridge, Phillips, afterwards to succeed him, was his contemporary in Dublin, Murchison learnt his first lesson in the field with him, Lyell was his pupil, Agassiz a co-adjutor, and Conybeare his nearest friend.

When Buckland was appointed Reader in Geology, the foundations of the science were already laid, but great problems remained for solution. The question of the Deluge and how far its effects could be recognized in the structure of the earth's crust was still one of these.

Buckland appeared at first as a champion of the Deluge: thus in his inaugural lecture delivered before this university in 1819 he expressed himself in the following words: "The grand fact of an universal deluge at no very remote period is proved on grounds so decisive and incontrovertible, that had we never heard of such an event from Scripture or any other Authority, Geology of itself must have called in the assistance of some such catastrophe to explain the phenomena of diluvian action."

Subsequently pursuing his researches into this question, he seems to have ransacked the whole world for evidence and found everywhere confirmatory proofs. The ancient gravels of Wytham were, he considered, swept from Warwickshire and counties still further North, in the rush of the great flood; stones from Norway were carried to the east coast of England, and the mass of pebbles and other *débris*, which were driven along with it, scoured the face of the country, and thus produced the polishing and striation so frequently visible on the surface of the harder rocks of our islands; the bones of mammoths and other mighty monsters of prediluvial times, that lie buried in the caves and elsewhere, were eloquent in their testimony to the destruction which it wrought on the living world. ... The "Reliquiae Diluvianae", in which these views appear, was published in 1823, and by its skill, learning and eloquence at once attracted universal admiration.

But Buckland, though he appears in this work as an advocate, was by no means merely an advocate; his was a

mind too highly endowed to rest satisfied with any but the most convincing
proof, and as time elapsed, and he
extended his researches, the evidence,
which he so industriously accumulated,
so far from strengthening his position,
began to gradually undermine it, and
already in 1837 [1836], when he published his great work on *Geology and
Mineralogy Considered with Reference to
Natural Theology*, we find him wavering.
While still asserting the occurrence of a
diluvial catastrophe, he was prepared to
abandon the view, which would connect
this with the Noachian deluge. "It has
been justly argued," he writes, "that as
the rise and fall of the waters of the
Mosaic deluge are described to have
been gradual and of short duration,
they would have produced comparatively little change on the surface of the
country they overflowed. ... This important point, however, cannot be considered as completely settled till more
detailed investigations of the newest
members of the Pliocene and of the
diluvial and alluvial formations shall
have taken place."

Scarcely a year had elapsed after this opinion had been expressed when investigations were commenced which were to cast a flood of light on the question from an unexpected quarter. Agassiz in 1838 was already engaged in those observations on the glaciers of Switzerland, and had commenced that series of brilliant discoveries which eventually culminated in a clear and reasonable explanation of the so-called diluvial phenomena. Buckland's study of these phenomena in Europe and the British Isles had rendered him the first authority of the time on this subject, though the cause of these phenomena, as we now know, was really not diluvial as he then imagined, but glacial. Buckland therefore was perfectly familiar with all the signs now recognized as characteristic of ice-action, no man more so; consequently when Agassiz took him over the glaciers of Switzerland, and showed him these agents actually at work, smoothing, polishing and striating the surface over which they flowed, the evidence was presented to a mind already prepared to appreciate it, and a few days' personal investigation sufficed to convince Buckland of the truth of Agassiz' opinions. This was not a case of a mere tyro, introduced to the subject for the first time, but of a skilled and trained observer, familiar by experience with results, the cause of which he had for long been trying vainly to discover.

How justly Buckland estimated the importance of this great discovery is shown by notes in his handwriting, that were probably used to assist him in one of those remarkable speeches the echoes of which still reverberate in our time. In one he says: "For some time to come the glacial theory must occupy a prominent place in geological investigation. The subject appears to me the most important that has been put forth since the propounding of the Huttonian theory; and the surface of the whole globe must be examined afresh with the view of ascertaining how far the effects of glaciers and ice-bergs and of floods produced by melting ice and snow can be found and identified with the actual effects of ice and snow in our present polar and alpine regions." In another note Buckland comments on "The vast field of new enquiry which the introduction of the glacial period between our epoch and the newest Tertiary opens to geological enquiry. The fact of the greater part of Europe and North America having for many years been sealed up under a cover of frozen snow converted to the state of glaciers is certain. ... Thus the flood that caused the Diluvium which in my 'Bridgewater Treatise' [*Geology and Mineralogy*, 1836] I have put back to the latest of the many Geological Deluges, was probably due to the melting of the ice. The details of this ice flood will fill a volume and will constitute Vol. II of my 'Reliquiae Diluvianae et Glaciales', which for fifteen years has been retarded for lack of the grand key which Agassiz has supplied in his 'Études des Glaciers'."

Thus Buckland courageously recanted his earlier opinions on the Deluge; and of the Noachian deluge as a geological agent, from this time onward we hear no more.

In 1840, we find the so-called obscurant-ist Dean a vehement defender not of the Universal Deluge but of the Ice Age. The scene is a "warm" and lengthy meeting of the Geological Society in November. The time is a quarter before midnight. What a meeting! Agassiz, Lyell and Buckland tell-ing veteran geologists that once upon a time enormous post-Pliocene glaciers had flourished in Great Britain. Agassiz further maintained that the northern hemisphere had been buried beneath great sheets of ice, like Greenland at the present day.

The opponents poured scorn on the proofs that the striated and polished rock-surfaces were the work of glacial ice.[1]

But Buckland was in fine fettle, and his "exposition of the doctrine of the glacial theory concluded—not, as we expected, by lowering his voice to a well-bred whisper, 'Now to', etc.—but with a look

[1] British geologists did not at first follow Agassiz in this explanation for the extensive lowland gravels, erratic blocks and clay deposits. For a couple of decades they hotly debated their own interpretations of these deposits by grounded ice-bergs, sudden but widespread land submergence and "waves of translations". Murchison said in 1843: "I cannot bring my mind to advocate that extent of glacial action in which my friend Dr Buckland believes". Years later, Professor Bonney declared: "It is to Dr Buckland we owe the recognition of the action of glaciers in this country."

and tone of triumph he *pronounced* upon his opponents who dared to question the orthodoxy of the scratches, and grooves, and polished surfaces of the glacial mountains (when they should come to be d—d) the pains of eternal itch without the privilege of scratching!"[1]

Buckland died in 1856. He had done so much for the advancement of the science of geology that the president (Colonel Portlock), in his address to the Geological Society in 1857, gave a long and full recognition to the value of his work. He ended with the words:

> I here close my remarks on the labours of Dr Buckland, and I now think it desirable to point out in the strongest light those high qualities which he possessed in no ordinary degree, namely, candour and freedom from prejudice.[2]

As a conclusion to this chapter it may be relevant to quote Prestwich who, in the introductory remarks of his famous paper of 1859, gives the prevalent opinion on the

[1] *The History of the Geological Society*, 1907, p. 142.
[2] *JGSL*, vol. 13 (1857), p. xliv.

value of the evidence for the parity or dis-
parity in age of animal and human fossil
remains:

Few strata have been more extensively
worked than the superficial sands, clays,
gravels, and brick-earth belonging to
the Drift or Pleistocene series, and a
great number of cave deposits belonging
to the same period have also been
carefully explored; nevertheless it is only
in a few exceptional cases that the
remains of man or of his works have
been recorded as occurring in association with the mammalian and other
organic remains so often found in such
situations, and even these few have
generally been viewed with doubt or
else rejected. The conclusion, in fact,
that man did not exist until after the
latest of our geological changes and until
after the dying out of the great extinct
mammals, had become almost a point
of established belief.

Although resting mainly upon negative evidence and preconceived opinion,
this prevalent belief was strengthened by
the failure of the many ill-observed and

dubious cases which had, from time to time, been brought forward. Owing to these circumstances there is little doubt that cases really meriting inquiry have been neglected or overlooked.

EPILOGUE

It is of interest to recapitulate what later authorities have to say on some of those early discoveries of human fossil bones. Their vacillating opinions seem to show that there was some excuse, before 1859, for the hesitation of the adverse critics to accept the antiquity of man on the evidence of those discoveries.

In 1823 Ami Boué, a well-practised geologist, disinterred many bones of a human skeleton from the face of a cliff, in undisturbed loess at Lahr in the Valley of the Rhine. In the vicinity, the loess of the same age contained remains of extinct animals. Boué brought a boxful of the finds to Cuvier at Paris. But the great anatomist affirmed his belief that they came from a burial-ground; and, apparently in connection with this discovery, made the famous statement: "Tout porte à croire que l'espèce humaine n'existait point." Forty years later Lyell wrote to Boué for the details, and gives all the information in the second edition of his *Antiquity of Man*. He had "no hesitation" in declaring his opinion that the antiquity of the remains "is fully borne out by the facts".[1] The latest verdict is by Boule in *Les Hommes Fossiles*: "No accurate observation, no decisive geological evidence justified the assertion of their high antiquity. ..."[2] Neither the condition of the deposit nor the morphological characters of the bones themselves justify us in regarding them as authentic fossil remains."[3]

About the same date as the Lahr discovery, Buckland investigated the Paviland cave. Professor W. J. Sollas made this the subject of his Huxley Memorial Lecture delivered to the Royal Anthropological Institute in 1913. To him for this enjoyable lecture may be applied the

[1] C. Lyell, *The Geological Evidences of the Antiquity of Man*, 2nd ed., appendix c, p. 338.
[2] M. Boule and H. V. Valois, *Fossil Men*, London, 1957, p. 6.
[3] Boule and Valois, p. 178.

words of praise that he bestows on Buckland. "News of these doings brought Buckland down from Derbyshire to carry out that admirable exploration which is described with the master's accustomed skill in the classic pages of the *Reliquiae Diluvianae*."[1] Buckland, as was said on page 55, had unearthed a skeleton coloured by red ochre, with ornaments of bone and ivory: he believed it was that of a woman. Afterwards he placed it in the Oxford University Museum, where it became known as the Red Lady. Falconer, in 1858, followed Buckland in attributing the interment to Romano-British times. Lartet and Christy (1863), fresh from Perigord, inspected the remains and at once agreed that all the facts corresponded with those they had observed at Cro-Magnon. In 1874 Boyd Dawkins, laying special stress on the disturbed condition of the cave deposits and on the presence of bones of sheep, reaffirmed Buckland's conclusion. "The interment is relatively more modern than the accumulation with remains of the extinct mammalia."[2]

[1] W. J. Sollas, *Paviland Cave: An Aurignacian Station in Wales: The Huxley Memorial Lecture for* 1913), London, 1913, p. 1.
[2] Boyd Dawkins, *Cave Hunting*, London, 1874, p. 234.

So the matter rested for nearly forty years, when Cartailhac, in 1911, inspected the remains of the Red Lady, and declared his belief that the interment was not only Palaeolithic, but, more precisely, was of Aurignacian age. Next year Professors Breuil and Boule made a careful examination of the bones, the ornaments and the flint implements. In their opinion the skeleton was Cro-Magnon and the paraphernalia Aurignacian. Sollas and Brueil then journeyed to the actual cave in Wales, where they found additional evidence to confirm this conclusion. Sollas was urged by his companion to undertake a complete exploration with the view of publishing a full account. This was the subject of his lecture. The Red Lady is now revealed as a genuine Palaeolithic *man*.

The classification of the skull discovered by Schmerling in the cave at Engis, near Liége, has likewise had its ups and downs. Lyell visited Liége in 1833 and met Schmerling, who showed him his splendid collection. Yet he doubted the antiquity of the fossil human bones. Among them must have been the Engis skull. It is figured in Schmerling's book. Lyell revisited

Liége in 1860 and he tells us in his *Antiquity of Man* (1863)[1] that he saw the skull in the town museum. He devotes several pages to all the circumstances of its discovery and now agrees it is "unequivocally ancient". He pays great tribute to Schmerling's extensive and laborious explorations of forty caves and the excellence of his published work, all of which were treated with indifference by the scientists of the day. Schmerling died in 1836 at the age of forty-five, worn out by his work; and the unsold copies of his valuable *Recherches sur les ossemens fossiles* were disposed of as waste paper. Lyell laments that he, in 1833, "a passing traveller failed to stop and scrutinize the evidence". Perhaps this is why John Phillips, in his review of Lyell's *Antiquity of Man*, ended with the words, "Sir C. Lyell was not able to accept the conclusion in 1833, but he received it without doubt in 1860. Singular change! that he who could resist the keen logic of the living discoverer, fresh from his diggings, should after thirty years, yield to the dry statements in the half-forgotten book which records the discoveries."

[1] pp. 79-92.

A decade later, Boyd Dawkins states in his book, *Cave Hunting* (1874), that the Engis skull "was obtained from a mass of breccia, along with bones and teeth of mammoth, rhinoceros, horse, hyena and bear; and subsequently M. Dupont found in the same spot a human ulna, other human bones, worked flints, and a small fragment of coarse earthenware. The discovery of this last is an argument in favour of the human remains being of a later date than the extinct mammalia".[1] Keith tells us (*Antiquity of Man*, 1915) that his friend Dr Rutot and Professor Fraipont again examined the skull in 1909, and the former was inclined to place it in the list of doubtful specimens. But he himself was in its favour: "There is no instance of Neolithic man having dug a hole in the hard breccia of a cave floor and buried his dead at a depth of five feet".[2] But Boule (*Les Hommes fossiles* 2nd ed., 1923) still repeats that the best anthropologists attribute it to Neolithic times. This verdict, however, is now reversed by Charles Fraipont's memoir *Les Hommes fossiles*

---

[1] Dawkins, pp. 234-5.
[2] *The Antiquity of Man*, London, 1915, p. 51.

d'Engis (1936); the skulls found by Schmerling, he says, are really those of fossil men.

Two very active cave explorers in the South of France who, in the time of MacEnery, received considerable notice, were Tournal and De Christol. Tournal, in 1828, found in the Grotte de Bize human bones and teeth, together with fragments of rude pottery, in the same mud and breccia with bones of extinct animals. A year later De Christol described the Cavern of Pondres filled up to the roof with mud and gravel in which were bones of an extinct hyena and rhinoceros, and also those of man. In it were fragments of two kinds of pottery, the coarser type being below the level of the extinct animals. These discoveries, which at the time received much attention, now receive only honourable mention because of the pottery.

One last example is the famous "fossil man of Denise" (1844). It occasioned an astonishing amount of discussion and controversy. The remains were dug up by a peasant in his vineyard in the volcanic ash breccia, near the town of Le Puy-en-Velay, in Central France. It was a "bone of contention" at the meeting of the Scientific

Congress of France at Le Puy in 1856.
There were experts for every opinion:
Were the bones a skilled counterfeit? Did
the fossil prove even a higher antiquity of
man than was usually proclaimed? Three
years later—the famous year, 1859—Lyell
made a special visit to Le Puy to investi-
gate the authenticity of the bones and
their geological age. His 1863 book devotes
six pages to the notorious bones; but he
seems to be very careful about commit-
ting himself to any definite opinion. Boule
dismisses the fossil man of Denise. "The
antiquity of these remains has been disputed. In the course of my geological
studies in the Velay (1909), I devoted
much care to the question of their age, or
rather of the age of the deposit in which
they were found. Having examined the
layer several times, I am of opinion that
this deposit dates back to a very remote
period of Quarternary times. But perhaps
it would be well not to discard the hypothesis of an artificial burial." The above
words are from the 1923 edition of his
book.[1] The 1957 translation hints at the
possibility of fraud;[2] and that further

[1] pp. 141-2.   [2] p. 151.

investigations do not throw any fresh light on the problem.

This account of some of those early discoveries of fossil human bones may now be closed. They were once famous but now perhaps appear tedious and bewildering, like "old, unhappy, far-off things and battles long ago". But they show the truth of Huxley's warning, spoken after the first flush of excitement over the antiquity of man, not first to abuse our predecessors if they were over-cautious and then to attribute this discretion to blindness and prejudice.

BIBLIOGRAPHY

Agassiz, A., *Études sur les glaciers*, Neuchâtel, 1840.

Beche, H. T. de la, "On the geology of the Tor and Babbacombe Bays, Devon", in *TGSL*, vol. 3 (1829), pp. 161-70.

Blainville, H. M. D. de, *Ostéographie, ou description iconographique comparée du squelette et du système dentaire des cinq classes d'animaux vertébrès récents et fossiles pour servir de base à la zoologie et à la géologie*, Paris, 1841-55 ,3 vols.

Boule, M., *Les Hommes fossiles*, Paris, 1921.

Boule, M. and Vallois, H. V., *Fossil Men* (English trans. 5th ed. of *Les Hommes fossiles*) London, 1957.

Boyd Dawkins, W., *Cave Hunting*, London, 1874.

Buckland, W., "Account of an assemblage of Fossil Teeth and Bones of Elephant, Rhinoceros, Hippopotamus, Bear, Tiger, and Hyaena, and sixteen other animals; discovered in a cave of Kirkdale, Yorkshire, in the year 1821: with a comparative view of five similar caverns in various parts of England, and others on the Continent" (with plates), *PTRS* (1822), pp. 171-2 36.
Reliquiae Diluvianae, London, 1823.
Geology and Mineralogy considered with reference to Natural Theology, London, 1836, 2 vols.

Cuvier, G. L. C. F., *Discours sur les révolutions de la surface du globe*, Paris, 1825.

Evans, J., "Occurrence of flint implements in undisturbed beds of gravel, sand and clay", *AE*, vol. 38, pp. 289-292.
The Ancient Stone Implements, Weapons and Ornaments of Great Britain, London, 1872.

Falconer, H., *Palaeontological memoirs and notes. With a biographical sketch of the author*, compiled and edited by C. Murchison, London, 1868, 2 vols.

Fraipont, C., *Les Hommes fossiles d'Engis*, Paris, 1936.

Godwin-Austen, R. A. C., "On the Bone Caves of Devonshire", *PGSL*, vol. 3, pp. 286-7 (summary).
"On the Geology of the South-East of Devonshire", *TGSL*, vol. 6, pp. 433-89.

Gordon, Mrs, *Life and Correspondence of William Buckland, by his daughter*, London, 1894.

Home, Everard, "An Account of some fossil remains of the Rhinoceros, discovered by Mr Whitby, in a cavern inclosed in the limestone rock, from which he is forming the Breakwater at Plymouth", *PTRS*, 1817, pp. 176-82.

Joly, N., *L'Homme avant les métaux*, Paris, 1879.
Man before Metals (English trans. *L'Homme avant les métaux*), London, 1885.

Keith, A., *The Antiquity of Man*, London, 1915.

Lyell, C., *Principles of Geology*, first ed. London, 1830-3, 3 vols.
The Geological Evidences of the Antiquity of Man, London, 1863.

MacEnery, J., "Cavern Researches", *TDA*, vol. 3, pp. 191-482.

Oliver, G., *Collections, illustrating the history of the Catholic religion in the counties of Cornwall, Devon, Dorset, Somerset, Wiltshire and Gloucestershire*, London, 1857.

Owen, R., *A History of British Fossil Mammals and Birds*, London, 1846.

Pengelly, W., "The Literature of Kent's Cavern, Torquay", *TDA*, vol. 2 (1867-8), pp. 469-522; vol. 3 (1869), pp. 191-482; vol. 4 (1870-1), pp. 467-90; vol. 10 (1878), pp. 141-81.
A Memoir of William Pengelly of Torquay, geologist, with a selection from his correspondence, H. Pengelly, London, 1897.

Perthes, Boucher de M., *De la Création*, Abbeville, 1838-41, 5 vols.
Antiquités celtiques et antédiluviennes. Mémoire sur l'industrie primitive et les arts à leur origine, Paris, 1847-9.

Prestwich, Grace, *Life and Letters of Sir Joseph Prestwich, written and edited by his wife*, Edinburgh, 1899.
"Recollections of M. Boucher de

Perthes", in *Essays, Descriptive and Biographical*, London, 1901, pp. 73-92.

Prestwich, Joseph, "On the Occurrence of Flint Implements, associated with the remains of extinct mammalia, in undisturbed beds of a late geological period in France, at Amiens and Abbeville, and in England at Hoxne", *PTRS*, 1861, pp. 277-316.

Rigollot, M. J., "Mémoire sur des instruments en silex trouvés a Saint-Acheul (1854)", *Mém. de la Soc. des antiq. de Picardie*, vol. 14.

Schmerling, P. C., *Recherches sur les ossemens fossiles découverts dans les cavernes de la province de Liége*, Liége, 1833-4.

Sollas, W. J., *The Age of the Earth, and other geological studies*, London, 1905.
Paviland Cave: An Aurignacian Station in Wales: The Huxley Memorial Lecture for 1913, London, 1913.

Vivian, E., "Researches in Kent's Cavern, Torquay, with the original MS. memoir of its first opening, by the late Rev. J. MacEnery (long supposed to have been lost) and the Report of the Sub-Committee of the Torquay Natural History Society, in *Report of the British Association*, Cheltenham, 1856, pp. 78-80.

"On the earliest traces of Human Remains in Kent's Cavern", *Report of the British Association*, Cheltenham, 1856, pp. 119-22.

Whidbey, J., "A Further Account of fossil bones in caverns inclosed in the limestone rocks at Plymouth", *PTRS*, 1821, pp. 133-4.